The Helicopter Trial Flight Guide

Congratulations!

This is your first step into the wonderful
World of Aviation.

Your personal invitation to experience the
pleasure of being airborne.

Ruth Downey

Nothing in this manual supersedes any legislation, rules, regulations or procedures contained in any operational document issued by Her Majesty's Stationery Office, the Civil Aviation Authority, the Joint Aviation Authorities, ICAO, the manufacturers of aircraft, engines and systems, or by the operators of aircraft throughout the world.

The Helicopter Trial Flight Guide - Ruth Downey

Copyright 2007 © Pooleys Flight Equipment Ltd

ISBN 1-84336-094-2

Pooleys Flight Equipment Ltd
Elstree Aerodrome
Hertfordshire
WD6 3AW
England

Tel: 0208 953 4870
Fax: 0208 953 2512
www.pooleys.com

Author **Ruth Downey**

Ruth Downey is a well respected Type Rating Examiner (TRE), Instructor and Managing Director of Helicopter Services Limited at Wycombe Air Park, Bucks. She holds an ATPL(H) IR and regularly flies the AS355 and B206 for company charter. She started flying with a PPL(H) in 1997.

Editors

Ian MacGregor
BSc in Electronics Engineering. Following a distinguished career in electronics research and development, Ian started flying in 1990. With an ATPL(H) and 5000 hours total, he is now Chief Pilot at Fast Helicopters at Shoreham. Additionally he is an FIC Instructor, CPL Instructor, 170 Examiner and PPL Examiner.

Dorothy Pooley
Dorothy is an instructor and examiner with over 6000 hours, who runs fixed wing flying instructor courses at Shoreham. She is also a CAA Flight Instructor Examiner and holds a commercial helicopter licence.

Daljeet Gill
Daljeet is Head of Design & Development for Pooleys Flight Equipment. Editor of the Pooleys Private Pilots Guides by David Cockburn, Pre-flight Briefing (Aeroplanes & Helicopters), R/T Communications, Pooleys JAR Manuals plus many others. Daljeet has been involved with editing, typesetting and design for these publications. Graduated in 1999 with a BA (hons) in Graphic Design, she deals with marketing, advertising & design of our new products. She maintains our website and produces our Pooleys Catalogue annually.

The Helicopter School

Contents

Ruth Downey - Helicopter Instructor

Introduction

The average helicopter pilot may be completely biased, but views helicopter flight as the most compelling and addictive form of aviation. Many pilots started their own career with a helicopter Trial Lesson and quickly found themselves completely absorbed, and unable to talk about anything else. If you have received a Trial Lesson as a gift, or you are interested in the possibility of taking up flying training, you are sure to remember the first time you boarded a helicopter and the thrill of taking the controls yourself.

Generally, if you have never experienced any form of aviation, the first steps towards taking a trial flight, (which is actually an early flying lesson) may be daunting. You will be boarding a small helicopter with unfamiliar instrumentation, after a briefing from an experienced flight instructor... this book hopefully will go some way to explaining what you should expect, both from the flight and from your chosen flight training organisation.

The Lesson itself will consist of a short lecture, sometimes called a 'briefing', typically using white board and associated props. This will explain what will happen in the air, the effects of controls, and some general safety aspects, followed by a flight with your instructor. To enjoy your flight to the full, it is helpful to appreciate what is going on around you, both in the cockpit and outside. After a brief study of this book, you should be able to sit in the pilot's seat, recognise some of the instruments and understand what the controls do. It will not be necessary to learn every principle covered in this book; whatever questions you have can be covered thoroughly by your instructor on the day. Like most other industries, there are certain phrases that will trip off the instructor's tongue, that may sound alien. Remember, the only stupid question is the one you don't ask. Please also ensure to read the chapter entitled "The Day of the Flight" for some helpful tips before you arrive at the Training Centre.

Do not feel that you are already committing yourself to learn to fly, the main aim of the Trial Lesson should be to enjoy yourself. If however you do wish to take the experience further, you will find the recommendations on gaining your own Private Pilot's Licence and useful contact addresses at the end of this book. The course consists of a minimum of 45 hours flight training, and the good news is that your trial lesson may be logged as part of your flight training.

A training helicopter is small, light, and has the same flying controls as bigger commercial aircraft, however it will be much cheaper per flying hour, and as such will not have all of the refinements of a bigger helicopter. The most common helicopter to training schools is the Robinson R22, pictured on the cover, but you may also come across the Hughes 269 or Enstrom helicopter.

The Robinson R22 is made by the Robinson Helicopter Corporation in Torrance, California. The R22 has two seats and dual controls fitted. This factory also produces the R44, pictured, which has four seats, one for the pilot and three passenger seats.

R44 Helicopter

Some helicopter training schools offer the R44 for trial lessons also. In most cases pilots learn to fly on the R22, and progress to the R44 as part of their advanced tuition.

Whichever helicopter your chosen training school prefers, the helicopters will be relatively straightforward to fly, with the minimum of cockpit instrumentation. Your first attempt at hovering may leave you feeling a little daunted, but probably hooked and eager to try again. Remember, it takes several hours of training to master the hover.

For most schools, after a fleet of trusty helicopters, the next most important factor are the instructors. Flight Instructors are highly trained, having been through an arduous training process, an intensive course of flying and hundreds of ground school hours. They must also maintain a strict training and competency programme, and must be a holder of a Civil Aviation Authority 'Class One Medical', certifying them as fit to fly. They will be led by a Chief Flying Instructor, who may also be the school examiner.

The school itself will have been approved for flight training by the Civil Aviation Authority (CAA). The CAA is the governing body for all flight training and commercial standards in the UK, covering all aspects from Engineering Standards to Flight Crew Licensing, Training Standards, Flight Crew Medicals and Flight Operations. All schools will be pleased to show you their approval certificates, if not already on display.

Finally, and probably most importantly, the engineering department is always around for back-up purposes. The helicopters themselves are maintenance intensive, and receive rigorous checks at regular intervals, to high standards, again set by the Civil Aviation Authority in conjunction with the aircraft manufacturer.

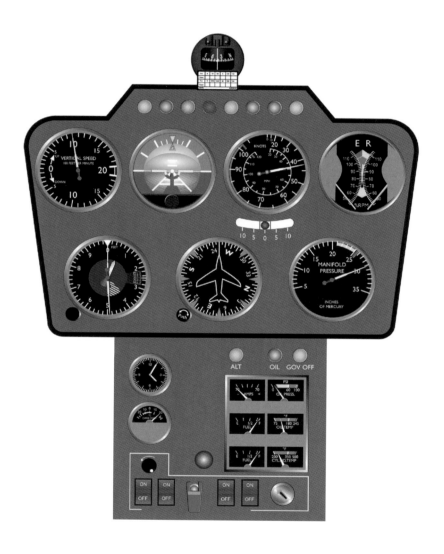

R22 Helicopter Instrument Panel

Helicopter Principles of Flight

To keep an aircraft in the air a force is needed. This force is known as lift. All aircraft use a device known as an aerofoil section, or wing and the helicopter is no exception. The wing is in the shape of an aerofoil, designed in such a way that air meeting the aerofoil has to pass a greater distance over the top of the section, than under the bottom. The air passing over the top speeds up, so that it arrives at the trailing edge at the same time as the airflow underneath. Because of the increased speed of the airflow, the pressure is lower above the aerofoil section than below. When enough airspeed is generated, the wing is sucked into this low pressure area. So picture a fixed wing aircraft gathering speed down a runway, once the correct speed has been achieved, the aeroplane will lift into the air. The helicopter rotates the blades on top of the helicopter fuselage, providing the aerofoil sections with the necessary speed, and therefore opposing airflow to provide lift. By increasing the angle at which the blades meet the air the helicopter will get more lift, enough to balance the weight of the helicopter, as in a stationery hover, or climb vertically.

You might remember as a child that you put your arm outside your father's motorcar, and you may have noticed the difference between holding your palm out flat, and then tilting it, whereupon it would have sailed into the air, demonstrating greater lift with a greater 'angle of attack'.

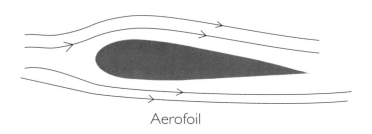

Aerofoil

R22 Helicopter

The Cyclic

In order to understand the use of the cyclic we need to consider that with the rotors turning we have a disc, referred to as the rotor disc. The attitude of the rotor disc is controlled by changing the angle of each blade cyclically using the cyclic stick. In doing so, lift is produced by the blades and total rotor thrust moves as shown below. Therefore if the cyclic is moved forwards the rotor disc tips forwards, the aircraft pitches nose down and starts to move forwards and accelerate. Conversely, aft cyclic will cause the helicopter to slow down. In forward flight we are using the cyclic to control our speed. Lateral cyclic tilts the cyclic right or left in the natural sense and is used to control the heading or direction of travel.

The joy, of course whilst flying your helicopter, is the ability to move in any direction from the hover and it is the use of the cyclic control that makes this possible.

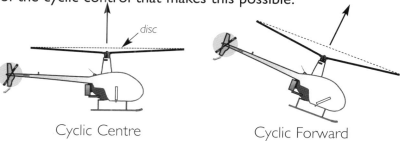

Cyclic Centre   Cyclic Forward

Collective Lever

The collective lever changes the pitch of the blades, collectively. That is to say, to change the angle of attack of the blades at the same time. With greater pitch on the blades, the helicopter will ascend. This is achieved quite simply by raising the lever with your left hand. It is situated in all helicopters by the pilot's seat. The action of lowering the lever will take pitch off the blades collectively and the helicopter will produce less lift and therefore descend. Because the helicopter requires more power to lift the helicopter and oppose the weight of the aircraft, passengers, fuel etc, as you raise your collective lever, you are also demanding more power from the engine. See page 17 for the power gauge, the 'Manifold Pressure Gauge'. Lowering the lever will reduce the power.

In most helicopters, the throttle is an integral part of the collective lever. The helicopter engine and rotor system operates at constant speed or revolutions per minute (RPM). The instrument pictured above the manifold pressure gauge is from a Robinson R22 helicopter, showing engine 'E' and rotor 'R' rpm, which are evenly matched. The green arc is where the engine and rotor rpm should be at all times during flight.

Nowadays there is an electronic governor, which keeps the rpm at the top of the green arc, but not all helicopters have this, some must be manually operated. The device is mainly to stop the helicopter being over-revved, but makes the helicopter very easy to fly, since it allows you to concentrate on the controls without worrying unduly about engine management.

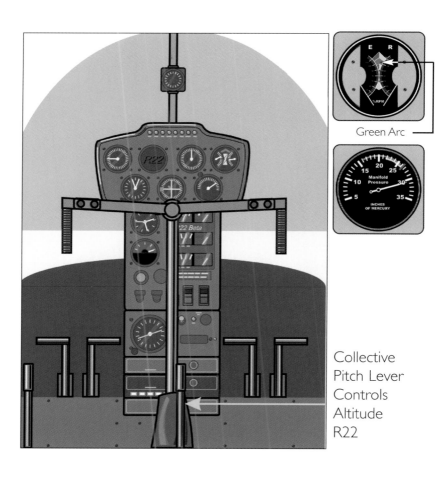

Green Arc

Collective
Pitch Lever
Controls
Altitude
R22

Needless to say, your left hand will be controlling the collective lever, so your right hand is used to control the cyclic stick. Just two limbs left!

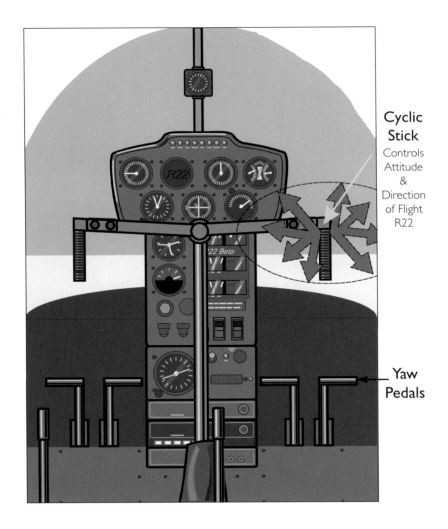

Cyclic Stick
Controls Attitude & Direction of Flight R22

Yaw Pedals

The action of the engine driving the rotor blades in one direction, will cause an 'equal and opposite reaction' (cast your mind back to Newton's Third Law). This reaction is the helicopter fuselage

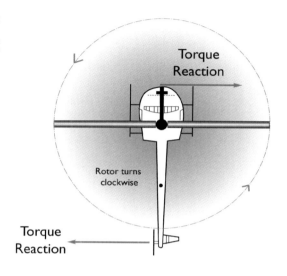

rotating in the opposite direction of rotor spin. This effect is exacerbated by power, the more power applied the more the 'Torque Reaction'. Hence, as you are pulling power to lift off from the ground, the helicopter fuselage will try to turn to the right, in an R22 for example. There are various forms of correction for this effect.

The most common method is the 'Tail Rotor' which is a system exactly like the main rotor assembly, but smaller and fitted on the back of the tail in the vertical plane. The yaw pedals operated by the pilots' right and left feet give the pilot control of the tail rotor, increasing and decreasing pitch as necessary, to give full control in the yawing plane, or allowing the pilot to manoeuvre the helicopter around its vertical axis. Other methods include contra-rotating discs as employed by the Chinook helicopter, thereby cancelling the need for a tail rotor, or by producing the force using air flow across the tail boom such as used by the Hughes 'Notar' helicopter. Another method is the so called 'fenestron', such as in the Gazelle.

R22 Helicopter

As with many other sports, flights are at the mercy of the weather. Generally in the UK, flights carry on all year round, however there will be some conditions in which it would not be sensible or safe to fly. Of major concern is the visibility. As you would not drive your Porsche on the motorway at ridiculous speeds in fog for fear of hitting something, you would not go out in conditions of poor visibility in your light aircraft. To the observer on the ground sometimes the weather looks fine, but it is always worth checking with the operations staff at the training centre, to save a wasted trip. What may look like bright blue skies in the area of your home town, could be patches of fog at the airfield, or reduced visibility in rain. High winds will also stop flights, most training schools impose a 'wind' or 'weather limit' on their flights, written into the Operations Manual as a matter of policy, so please do check before you leave.

Clothing is an important factor, most importantly you need to be comfortable. Airfields are often windy places, being large open fields, and you may be required to board the helicopter after a short walk over soft ground. High heels, hats, baggage and umbrellas are not recommended.

If for any reason you are feeling unwell, please do not hesitate to contact the office immediately, it would be best to fly another day. Of course as much notice as you can give the school is appreciated, especially at weekends or busy periods, so that they may release the helicopter for somebody else to fly. The Chief Instructor will have the last say on safety, and will not allow any person who has been drinking alcohol to board an aircraft. Even the slightest amount may have adverse effects at altitude, and hangovers are not conducive to an enjoyable flight!

Also on a more personal note, for some types of helicopters there may be a weight restriction. For safety, the pilot will not take off with an overweight helicopter, since control movements may be restricted, and the safety of the aircraft would be jeopardised. Generally, when your trial lesson is purchased, the operations staff will tactfully ensure that the recipient of the voucher does not exceed the stated seat weight. Hughes 300 helicopters take more weight than the R22 for example, do beware!

If you are in any doubt at all, call the operations staff at the office, they are there to help you.

After checking in with the reception at your chosen training centre, you will be ushered with your companions to a quiet office or briefing room where the instructor can brief you on the principles of flight and safety details for the flight itself. Some schools brief at the aircraft. Safety is of course the most important feature of any briefing, and certain items will definitely be highlighted. Firstly the way you approach the helicopter is important. Mostly the student will be taken to the helicopter by the instructor, and will sit in the helicopter whilst it is started and shut down at the end of the lesson. Less commonly, rotors running changes may happen, where you will be escorted to and from the helicopter with the engine running and the rotors turning. Whichever method is used, it is always advisable to approach the helicopter towards the nose, or in a position where the pilot can see you, and keep your head down at all times. If the rotors are running, the tail rotor is exceptionally dangerous, so be sure to approach the helicopter as instructed.

Your companions will be looked after by the office staff, and will not be allowed to wander around in the dispersal or parking area, but will be accompanied whilst they watch you take off. Cameras are always welcome, and poses allowed next to the helicopters with the rotor blades safely stopped. You will also be allowed to take a camera with you on the flight; have a word with your instructor first, he or she will willingly take the controls for a short while. It may even be possible to direct the track of the flight to the vicinity of your home, however most short trial lessons will generally take place around the airfield.

Following this, the briefing will consist of additional safety details. The pilot will be in touch with Air Traffic Control at all times, and if he is addressed will be required to answer the call immediately, so he may well brief you that should he need to talk to the 'Tower', he may require you to keep quiet for a brief period. Headsets are worn in the cockpit, so you will be able to talk to the instructor with the same ease as he can talk to the Tower. You will notice your instructor depress a button on the cyclic stick to communicate with the Tower, but in most helicopters you can talk to each other without the need to push any button. Whilst the air traffic communications may sound like a foreign language at first, with a few hours practice at radio telephony the phrases used will become routine. It also helps when you anticipate what the Tower will say. At times you will notice the instructor will look as if he is not listening, but is able to respond immediately when his call sign, or aircraft registration is used. However don't worry, you will not be expected to use the radio to talk to the Tower during your trial lesson.

The second part of the briefing will be on the effects of controls, associated instrumentation, and probably a few details about the helicopter, build, manufacture and history. At this point your instructor will be pleased to answer any questions.

The question most people ask is 'What happens if the engine fails?' The most common misconceptions surround this area, some people think that if the engine fails the helicopter will plummet towards the earth with disastrous consequences. This is not the case at all, and at some stage during your flight, and with your approval, the instructor will be pleased to demonstrate a simulated engine failure by putting the aircraft into 'Autorotation'. He will close the throttle, and maintain the rotors at the right speed by the rate of descent airflow, or the updraft caused by the helicopter descent. If he elects to per-form an 'engine-off landing' he will reduce the airspeed of the helicopter at around 30 feet by gently 'flaring' the helicopter and cushion the touchdown with the collective lever. If you prefer, he will be able to re-introduce the power before the landing is performed, a 'power-recovery'. Instructor pilots spend a great deal of time practising these maneouvres and are always pleased to illustrate the engine-off characteristics of their helicopter. Do remember that this procedure is merely demonstrated, the engine is not really stopped, but remains at 'idle' (ie. like tick-over in your car)and may be brought back up to the normal flight revolutions at any time.

Once the flight commences, the helicopter may well have to be positioned to a training area, or safe take off area, clear of the fixed wing runway and other aircraft. This is called 'hover-taxying' which means lifting the helicopter into the hover, and moving in a controlled manner to the correct airfield destination at approximately five feet above the ground. All airfields will have a slightly different procedure, and your pilot will be careful to comply with the air traffic patterns. Also around the aerodrome the traffic procedures will be closely adhered to. For example, the helicopter circuit may be at 800 feet above the ground level (or aerodrome QFE) and the fixed wing circuit pattern at 1200 feet above ground level, to ensure that there are no conflictions.

Enjoy your flight!

Artificial Horizon or Attitude Indicator

The Artificial Horizon is not an essential part of the instrumentation of the training helicopter and many do very well without. Those helicopters fitted with the instrument are used for 'instrument' training, which is to say flight in instrument  (cloud) or poor visibility conditions. At the end of a PPL(H) course, students are taught to use the instrument in case of inadvertent flight into low visibility conditions.

The Artificial Horizon is a gyro, which spins up to around twenty thousand revolutions per minute. It is known as an 'earth tied' gyro, which describes its function very nicely. The markings on the top indicate your angle of bank or turn, ten, twenty or thirty degrees.

Remember the helicopter is to be flown visually, the instruments should not be stared at during your trial lesson which will be flown in visual meteorological conditions (VMC), but are useful for back-up purposes and whilst training.

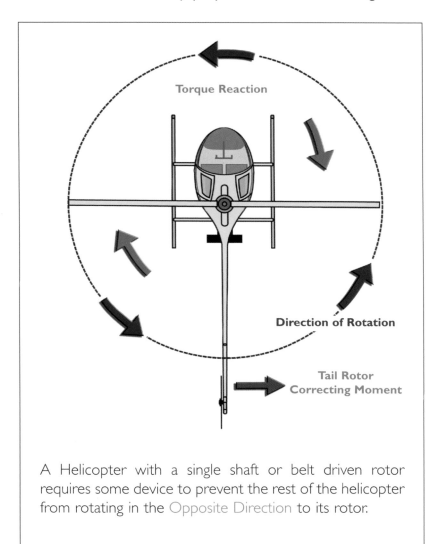

Torque Reaction

Direction of Rotation

Tail Rotor
Correcting Moment

A Helicopter with a single shaft or belt driven rotor requires some device to prevent the rest of the helicopter from rotating in the Opposite Direction to its rotor.

The Air Speed Indicator is an air driven instrument, showing your speed through the air. Air is taken through a small tube called a 'pitot' tube which is found on the helicopter, generally on the rotor mast fairing on 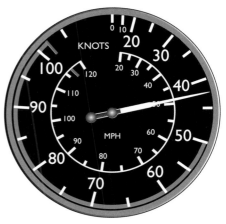 the front, or somewhere in the air stream. This collects 'dynamic' pressure, or the pressure due to movement of the helicopter through the air. The air is fed into an airtight casing, which also has a static pressure source, and small bellows, a stack of two or three pressure responsive capsules which expand or contract, moving a needle around a calibrated dial. The needle records dynamic pressure, which is proportional to airspeed. On the R22 the dial shows knots and miles per hour.

Also to be found on the helicopter is a static source of air which feeds the instruments. This is generally a clear tube which is placed out of the airstream. On an R22 helicopter it is to be found inside the faring below the auxiliary fuel tank, protected from the dynamic flow of air.

R44 Helicopter Instrument Panel

Vertical Speed Indicator

In the Vertical Speed Indicator, the static air is fed into small bellows in an airtight casing, which is filled with static air of its own. The pressure drops as the aircraft ascends, so the bellows collapse, and the needle indicates an  upward trend. Only when the static pressure affects both sides equally does the indicator read zero. As in all air-driven instruments, the workings are not instantaneous, there is a short time lag.

R44 Helicopter Cockpit

The Altimeter records the height of the aircraft above ground level, or above sea level, by measuring the air pressure. It is actually just an accurate barometer. Whilst this is different every day, the pressure

reduces with height at the same rate. The Air Traffic Control tower will give the pressure setting for the height of a known datum, generally the middle of the airfield's longest runway. Pressure settings may also be given for the height above sea level. If using the QFE or 'Field Elevation' you will notice your instructor set the altimeter to zero, and from then on the altimeter will record the height above the airfield. Whilst in the circuit most pilots use the QFE. When leaving the circuit, most helicopter pilots will fly on the QNH, or 'Nautical Height', the height above sea level. It is important in a busy airfield circuit that all pilots have their pressure correctly set, since airfields will generally have a traffic pattern, involving differing types of aircraft at different heights.

For example, as mentioned previously, fixed wing aeroplanes in the circuit at 1000 feet above the airfield, and helicopters at 700 feet above ground.

Again the casing is sealed, but for the static pressure which is fed to the bellows. The pressure changes move the capsules up and down and through a system of linkages and gears the needle is moved around a dial calibrated in feet.

R44 Helicopter

Manifold Pressure Gauge

The power, applied by lifting the collective lever, is measured in the R22 by the Manifold Pressure Gauge, which measures the manifold 'depression'. The one pictured is measuring the ambient pressure, since the engine is

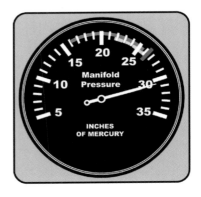

switched off. Once the engine is started your instructor will be careful not to exceed the red line.

R22 Helicopter Cockpit

R22 Helicopter

The Compass is usually mounted well above the instrument panel, to keep it away from the aircraft instruments and magnetic fields which can cause miscellaneous readings. Usefully, it is also mounted, on  the R22 at least, in the line of your eye. It reads 'Magnetic' headings which are a few degrees different from 'True' headings, so pilots will make a small correction when navigating. It is subject however to 'turning errors' which makes it difficult to read whilst turning the aircraft or climbing and descending, so some small helicopters will include the use of a Direction Indicator. This is a gyro instrument, more stable and easier to read.

R22 Helicopter

R22 Helicopter

Slip Indicator

This is simply a glass tube, similar to a bent spirit level, with a weighted ball in the bottom. The ball responds to gravity and will be displaced either left or right by centrifugal forces, thus showing the helicopter skidding or slipping into a turn. You will notice if the helicopter is flown, out of balance, or seems to be skidding through the air, that the weight of your body will be firmly on one side of your seat, instead of your normal seated position. This is termed Somatosensory information, or 'flying by the seat of your pants'. In any case, with a little practice you will able to feel if the helicopter should be balanced. If the ball is displaced to the right, you will need to press the right pedal, and so for the left. The 'balance ball' gives erroneous readings in the hover, and should be ignored when you are hovering or hover-taxying. There are also two pieces of string attached to the window frame which give an indication of balance when they are central.

Radios and Intercom

The radio is needed for communications with Air Traffic Control. This is important to obtain clearance for take-off and landing. You will hear lots of abbreviations and codes being spoken over the radio. There is a special "language" for the radio communications to ensure that valuable airtime is not wasted. Some of the abbreviations are set out in the glossary at the back of this book.

Typical Radio Set

Not only for your comfort, but in order to communicate with Air Traffic Control, other aircraft and your co-passengers, headsets are worn at all times during your trial lesson.

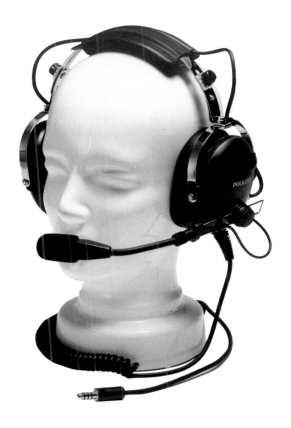

Pooleys Helicopter Headset

When most people first fly, they notice that whatever is said on the radio sounds like a foreign language. Certainly people wanting to take up helicopter flight think they will never begin to understand what is being said, or ever be able to converse with an Air Traffic Controller with anything other than a stutter. The reality is a very basic skill. A few procedures need to be adhered to, but otherwise experienced pilots can generally anticipate what is about to be said, which takes all of the hard work out of the communications. Student pilots sometimes need to overcome the stage fright, which comes from a common belief that when they press the button to talk, the entire world of radio is listening to them!

R22 Radio-Nav Equipment

It also helps if you are familiar with the procedures at the airfield you are visiting. Common to all pilots is 'Pooleys Flight Guide' which gives all the details of the United Kingdom aerodromes, plus a lot of other useful information. The table below is taken from the back page of 'Pooleys'.

The Phonetic Alphabet and Morse Code

ALPHA	• —	NOVEMBER	— •
BRAVO	— • • •	OSCAR	— — —
CHARLIE	— • — •	PAPA	• — — •
DELTA	— • •	QUEBEC	— — • —
ECHO	•	ROMEO	• — •
FOXTROT	• • — •	SIERRA	• • •
GOLF	— — •	TANGO	—
HOTEL	• • • •	UNIFORM	• • —
INDIA	• •	VICTOR	• • • —
JULIET	• — — —	WHISKY	• — —
KILO	— • —	X-RAY	— • • —
LIMA	• — • •	YANKEE	— • — —
MIKE	— —	ZULU	— — • •

Pooleys Learning Material for Helicopter Flying

- Pooleys Air Presentations - Technical 'H' Pilots Work Book
- Pooleys Air Presentations - Pre-flight Briefing 'H'
- Principles of Flight Technical 'H' - H R Quantick
- Pooleys Pilots Log Book

Where Next?

Your trial lesson was your first lesson, and all the time spent in the air with a properly qualified instructor, counts towards the course. If you do decide you need more time to consider, you may even start learning to fly, without being obliged to complete the course. However once started most people see the course through to its conclusion, and have their PPL licence issued by the Civil Aviation Authority.

The course itself has no time limits, save for the ground exams which must be completed within one year from the date of the first exam taken, more on the exams and ground school later. Some people take anything up to two years to complete the course, a full time course could take just one month. Everybody is different of course, with differing rates of learning, some people are much better practically than academically and vice versa. However it is generally considered that at least once a week is better in the early stages. Attempting to take lessons too infrequently will slow the rate of your progress, since you will need to spend time recapping on earlier exercises to remind yourself. Also your chosen school will advise you that too much in the early stages of learning can be very tiring so intensive training or very long lessons may not be conducive to steady progress.

The JAR PPL(H) course is 45 hours long and is made up of 27 exercises, including all of the skills that you may be asked to demonstrate to your examiner at the end of your course. These include such exercises as hovering, taking off and landing, quick stops, advanced autorotations, steep turns and many more. Five hours are dedicated to flying by sole reference to instruments. The 45 hours include at least 25 hours dual instruction and 10 hours solo. Most schools will insist that you complete all of the dual exercises before going solo. Some helicopter manufacturers recommend that a certain amount of air-time is completed before going solo. Whatever your school recommends for you personally, the solo experience is likely to be one you will never forget. Your very first solo will be closely supervised by your instructor, who will ensure that the weather is clement and not too windy, and your performance is up to the task! When he is comfortable that you are ready, he will then exit the helicopter, and leave you to complete a circuit, or some hovering exercises.

After your first solo, or perhaps even before it, you will also start learning about navigation. You will be working towards your solo cross-country qualifying flight, which will consist of a flight of at least 100 nautical miles, and two landings at two different airfields.

Meanwhile there are exams that must be completed:

Human Performance and Limitations
Air Law
Meteorology
Navigation
Flight Planning and Performance
Radio Telephony Theory
Radio Telephony Practical
Technical and Principles of Flight

These are not arduous, but quite straight forward multi choice papers, and most schools will offer some form of ground school or assistance to prepare you for the exams.

Indeed there are many useful publications that you will want to start reading immediately and some very useful equipment such as CDs etc. Pooleys Flight Equipment can supply everything that is needed for the budding PPL and experienced aviator. All you need to remember is to budget for some books and some ground school from a willing instructor.

You must be 14 years of age before logging any flight, and 16 years before going solo. Your licence will not be issued before you are 17 years of age.

Before you start on a PPL course, it is recommended that you obtain a medical Certificate. A PPL(H) will not be issued to you without it; you will need a 'Class 2' certificate from an Authorised Medical Examiner. Regretfully you cannot get this from your family GP, but must go to an examiner certified by the Civil Aviation Authority. Your chosen school will be able to advise you where the nearest one is.

Quite a lot to think about, I'm sure you will agree! Anyway, whatever you decide - have a great trial lesson.

JAR-FCL Helicopter PPL Syllabus & Pilot's Record of Training.

Glossary

Aerofoil

Shaped 'wing' section with curved upper surface
to promote lift

Altimeter

Instrument to measure pressure and height over a datum,
such as the airfield or sea level

Angle of Attack

Angle between the blade and the relative air flow

Artificial Horizon

Instrument used for control of the aircraft in the rolling
plane when in low visibility conditions

ASI

Air Speed Indicator

ATC

Air Traffic Control

CAA

Civil Aviation Authority – see also under 'useful addresses'

Circuit

The traffic pattern around the airfield from which to join and depart the airfield, and organise the landing order.

CPL(H)

Commercial Pilots Licence ((H) denotes Helicopters – (A) for Aeroplanes)

Drag

Opposite to thrust, the force produced by the aircraft as it passes through the air

Headsets

To be used when in communication with ATC and passengers

JAR

Joint Airworthiness Regulations (A set of rules agreed by a number of European States to encourage harmonisation of aviation matters between the member states)

Knot

The speed of one nautical mile per hour

Lift

Opposite to weight, force produced by air flow over an aerofoil

Mixture Control

Used to supply fuel to the engine and to stop the engine after flight

Slip Indicator

Slip Indicator or 'balance ball' shows amount of yaw, corrected with yaw pedals

Pitot Tube

Small tube collecting 'dynamic' air for pressure instruments-situated in main airstream

PPL(H)

Private Pilots Licence ((H) in brackets denotes Helicopters - (A) for Aeroplanes)

QFE

Pressure setting to be dialled into Altimeter to record height above the airfield or 'above ground level - (agl)'

QNH

Pressure setting for altitude above mean sea level (amsl)

Ts and Ps

Temperature and Pressure gauges used to assess the engine oil pressure & temperature amongst other things - and thus the health of the engine

Transponder

Electronic device to send height/altitude and location information to ground based radar systems

Throttle

Device for increasing and decreasing the fuel flow to the engine, thus engine and rotor revolutions

Thrust

The force created by the aerofoil section/rotors

VSI

Vertical Speed Indicator – shows rate of climb or descent

Yaw

The effect of the aircraft skidding sideways

Let's Fly!

Aeronautical Information Service (AIS)

NATS. AIS Central Office,
First Floor, Control Tower Building,
Heathrow Airport,
Hounslow, Middlesex. TW6 1JJ
Tel: 020 8745 3456
Fax: 020 8745 3453
e-mail: ais.supervisor@nats.co.uk
website: www.ais.org.uk

Aircraft Owners and Pilots Association (AOPA)

50a Cambridge Street,
London, SW1V 4QQ
Tel: 020 7834 5631
Fax: 020 7834 8623
e-mail: aopa@easynet.co.uk
website: www.aopa.co.uk

Air League

The Broadway House,
Tothill Street,
London, SW1H 9NS
Tel: 020 7222 8463
Fax: 020 7222 8462
e-mail: exec@airleague.co.uk
website: www.airleague.co.uk

British Helicopter Advisory Board,
Building C2, West Entrance, Fairoaks Airport,
Chobham, Woking, Surrey, GU24 8HX
Tel: 01276 856100
Fax: 01276 856126
e-mail: info@bhab.org
website: www.bhab.org

British Microlight Aircraft Association (BMAA)
Bullring, Deddington, Oxon, OX15 0TT
Tel: 01869 338888
Fax: 01869 336006
e-mail: general@bmaa.org
website: www.bmaa.org

British Women Pilots Association (BWPA)
Brooklands Museum, Weybridge, KT13 0QN
Tel: 01342 893739
e-mail: membership@bwpa.demon.co.uk
website: www.bwpa.co.uk

Civil Aviation Authority Safety Regulation Group,
Aviation House, Gatwick Airport South,
West Sussex, RH6 0YR
Tel: 01293 567171 (Switchboard) 01293 573700 (Licensing)
573685 (Medical) Fax: 01293 824014
e-mail: safety.general@srg.caa.co.uk
website: www.caa.co.uk

General Aviation Safety Council (GASCO)
Rochester Airport, Chatham, Kent, ME5 9SD
Tel: 01634 200203
Fax: 01634 200203
e-mail: info@gasco.co.uk
website: www.gasco.org.uk

Guild of Air Pilots and Air Navigators (GAPAN)
Cobham House, 9 Warwick Court, London, WC1R 5DJ
Tel: 020 7404 4032
Fax: 020 7404 4035
e-mail: gapan@gapan.org
website: www.gapan.org

Helicopter Club of Great Britain
Ryelands House, Aynho, Banbury, Oxon, OX17 3AT
Tel: 01869 810646
Fax: 01869 810755
e-mail: info@hcgb.co.uk
website: www.hcgb.co.uk

Pooleys Flight Equipment Ltd
Elstree Aerodrome, Hertfordshire, WD6 3AW
Tel: 020 8953 4870
Fax: 020 8953 2512
e-mail: sales@pooleys.com
website: www.pooleys.com

Popular Flying Association (PFA)
Turweston Aerodrome, Nr Brackley, Northants, NN13 5YD
Tel: 01280 846786
Fax: 01280 846780
e-mail: office@pfa.org.uk
website: www.pfa.org.uk

Royal Aero Club of the United Kingdom (RAeC)
Radford Barn, Radford Semele, Leamington Spa,
Warwickshire, CV31 1UT
Tel: 01926 332713
Fax: 01926 335206
e-mail: secretary@royalaeroclub.org
website: www.royalaeroclub.org

Royal Aeronautical Society
4 Hamilton Place, London, W1J 7BQ
Tel: 020 7499 3515
Fax: 020 7499 6230
e-mail: membership@raes.org.uk
website: www.raes.org.uk

Helicopter Pilot's Starter Kit

A First Class Starter Pack for the Helicopter Pilot

This pack contains the following items:-

Pre-Flight Briefing (H)

Principles of Helicopter Flight

Helicopter Pilots Manuals

Set of Air Pilot's Manuals (Vol.2. Vol.3. Vol.6. and Vol.7.)

Helicopter Question Bank Vol 3

Helicopter Key Facts Vol 3

Pooleys CRP-1 Computer

Pooleys PP-1 Protractor

Pooleys NM-2 Scale Ruler

Pooleys RNP-1 Plotter

Pooleys HB-1 Knee board and Log Pad

CAA 1:250,000 chart of your local area please specify area required.

Set of Lumocolour Markers

Pooleys Loose Leaf Flight Guide complete with annual amendments.

FC-1 Mini Courier Flight Case

Certificate of Completion
of a Helicopter

Trial Flying Lesson

This is to certify that

....

has piloted a helicopter on their own under the
guidance of a qualified flying instructor, and has
successfully completed:

....

....

Instructor (QHI) ....

Date ....